# Grammar

## Grammar

## Section 1 — Word Types

### Page 2 — Nouns

1. You should have circled: **sofa**, **idea**, **field**, **gang**, **Sally**, **people**, **education**, **socks**.
2. **Russia** is cold — proper noun
   get off the **table** — common noun
   green **cabbage** — common noun
   **Oliver** knows best — proper noun
   it took place in **March** — proper noun
   those **gentlemen** — common noun
   I live in **Liverpool** — proper noun
   this leaky **tent** — common noun
   I had a **dream** — common noun
   see you on **Friday** — proper noun

### Page 3 — Adjectives

1. You should have underlined: **lucky**, **scruffy**, **blue**, **huge**, **tired**, **bossy**
2. The **roaring** aeroplane tore across the sky.
   Lady Claire told her **lazy** butler to hurry up.
   The **magical** wizard cast a spell on the king.
   Lots of snails live in Mr Watson's **overgrown** garden.

### Page 4 — Verbs

1. Verbs: **prepare**, **create**, **know**, **grow**, **ask**, **feel**, **behave**, **discover**
2. Dad often **tries** to take an extra biscuit from the tin.
   We **are** driving to Stoke-on-Trent this Saturday.
   Dianne **crosses** the bridge to get to work.
   Karl **teaches** rock climbing at the village hall.
   On Wednesdays, Zola **goes** to chess club.

### Page 5 — Adverbs

1. Aunty May's special chocolates **mysteriously** disappeared.
   I **always** tell Gareth the whole truth.
   Mum said the postman would arrive **soon**.
   Neela **sometimes** walks to school, but **usually** drives.
2. Sam **greedily** ate three hamburgers.
   Look, I think that's John over **there**.
   Wendy and Bob go on holiday **tomorrow**.
   Felicity behaved rather **oddly** when she saw us.

### Pages 6 and 7 — Pronouns

1. Today I went to the cinema with Jane. We bought some popcorn and ate **it** all during the adverts. Jane talked through the whole film — **she** is a chatterbox. A man told **us** to be quiet — **he** was quite angry.
2. Rachel went out in the rain and **she** got wet.
   Neil and Liam looked for Liz until **they** found **her**.
   Dad and I found a ring, so **we** handed **it** in.
3. 'He' refers back to **James**.
   'Her' refers back to **Sally**.
   'It' refers back to **the wind**.
   'Them' refers back to **the trees**.
4. Yvonne wants to be an astronaut. **She** is very ambitious.
   Mr Morris hates cycling. **He** thinks **it** is (or **it's**) silly.

### Pages 8 and 9 — Possessive Pronouns

1. You should have circled: **yours**, **theirs**, **his**, **hers**, **mine**, **ours**.
2. Mrs Parkin's chocolate brownies taste better than **ours**.
   Harry can't find his bike, so Tim is giving him **his**.
   We could eat at my house or at **yours**.
   I told him it was **mine**, but he still took **it**.
   We tried, but **theirs** are just bigger than **ours**.
3. Whose is the ball? **His**
   Whose is the dog? **Theirs**
   Whose are the shoes? **His**
   Whose is the apple? **Hers**
   Whose is the teddy? **Hers**
4. Lucy needs a pen — you could give her **yours**.
   Paul thinks this is my bag — but it's **his**.
   Don't eat that sandwich — that's **mine**.
   Kareem needs a place to stay — he could stay at **ours**.

### Pages 10 and 11 — Articles and Determiners

1. At school, there was **a** dog in **the** playground. He ran around **the** children and barked at **a** teacher. He sniffed **the** grass and then went home. I've never seen **an** animal at playtime before.
2. **The** milkman left a note to say he's going on holiday.
   When **the** cake was ready, we decorated it with icing.
   Poppy and Silvia went on **a** walk across the fields.
   There was **an** unusual smell in the air.
   **The** ending of the story was disappointing.
3. **Some** friends of mine have been to **this** restaurant before.
   Charlie has **an** idea about how to rescue **your** dog.
   **Every** suggestion on how to tackle **my** problem is useful.
   **Those** police officers walked in and arrested **a** waiter.
4. Add **some** water — any amount will do.
   Every person in **this** room needs to think about it.
   **Those** children are scaring our neighbour's cat.
   I think **that** car has a flat tyre.
   **This** pie is the best pie in the world.
   **This** cake recipe says we need four bananas.

## Section 2 — Clauses and Phrases

### Pages 12 and 13 — Clauses

1. Main clauses: **Katie reads a lot**, **it has to go**
   Subordinate clauses: **when you're ready**, **unless you disagree**, **because he's got too much**

# Grammar

2. I sometimes watch TV while eating my breakfast.
   After the news has finished, Dad goes to bed.
   Although she is funny, Nicole can be quite annoying.
   We're going to go for a walk even if it rains.
3. If Julian doesn't arrive soon, I'm going without him.
   The boys don't mind school although the park is more fun.
   Edward went back to bed while I made him some soup.
   We're going out for dinner because it's Ben's birthday.
   Despite the bad weather, they had a great holiday.
4. They won't win their next match unless they train much harder.
   Jenny will call us when she's finished.
   He'll lend me a DVD if I lend him this game.
   I usually feel very full after a big meal.
   Hannah can't wait until it's her birthday.
5. Any suitable main clause.
   Examples:
   When I come home from school, **I have my dinner**.
   After I've cleaned my teeth, **I go to bed**.
   If Bill starts snoring, **I'll splash him with lemonade**.

### *Pages 14 and 15 — Noun Phrases*

1. Phrases: **unusually quiet**, **quite right**, **really clean**, **near to her**
   Noun phrases: **pretty horses**, **green jumper**, **sunbathing hippos**, **every hairdresser**, **the freshly cut grass**, **black, plastic boxes**
2. You should have circled: **shoes**, **comics**, **vase**, **house**, **alarm**.
3. Any suitable nouns.
   Examples:
   the interesting **programme** about wildlife
   the grumpy **goldfish** at the pet shop
   a greedy little **lamb** in the field
   the open packet of **crisps** on the floor
4. Any suitable adjectives.
   Examples:
   **green** fields
   a **long** walk
   some **curious** sheep
5. Any suitable prepositions.
   Examples:
   the railway line **under** the big bridge
   a black cat **next to** the road
   chocolate buttons **in** the sweetie jar

## Section 3 — Adverbial Phrases

### *Pages 16 and 17 — Adverbial Phrases*

1. I arrived at school much earlier than usual.
   He completed the work as quickly as possible.
   I can play the violin better than my brother.
   My sister ate her dinner really eagerly.
2. so suddenly
   quite carefully
   very softly
   extremely loudly
   unbelievably quickly
3. You should have ticked these sentences and underlined these adverbial phrases:
   I like to eat chocolate at the weekends.
   Twice a week I am allowed to eat crisps.
   I like to eat chocolate in the bath.
4. You should have ticked:
   whilst swimming
   extremely quietly
   around the room
   The sentences should read:
   She danced around the room.
   I whispered extremely quietly.
   Caroline got wet whilst swimming.

### *Pages 18 and 19 — Adverbial Phrases as Introductions*

1. On the way home**,** we visited Grandma and Grandad.
   Before breakfast**,** I went for a run.
   Very patiently**,** David built the tower of cards.
   After six years as a doctor**,** John left his job.
   All of a sudden**,** Helen stormed out.
   Last month**,** Molly started a new school.
2. Near the river, Jo built a tree house.
   Very angrily, Jack smashed the glass.
   Once a week, I buy a magazine.
3. You should have ticked:
   At school, people often confuse us.
   With care, we decorated the birthday cake.
   Corrected sentences:
   Every Sunday morning, I have pancakes.
   On the bottom shelf, there are three books.
4. Any sensible adverbial phrases used correctly.
   Examples:
   **After lunch**, we went for a walk.
   **On the table**, there's a bunch of flowers.
   **Quite nervously**, Jeremy began his speech.
   **Very bravely**, my dad rescued the rabbit.
5. Any sentence about the picture where an adverbial phrase is used correctly at the start of the sentence.
   Example:
   Ridiculously loudly, the baby screamed for its mum.

## Section 4 — Conjunctions and Prepositions

### *Pages 20 and 21 — Conjunctions*

1. I think I'll go to the shop, **and** I'll buy some bananas.
   We need a new computer, **for** our old one is broken.
   The weather was bad, **so** we didn't go for a walk.
   You can go home, **or** you can come with me.
2. Edgar was thirsty, **so** I poured him a drink.
   Tom likes chess, **and** he likes dancing.

CGP

# KS2 English

## Targeted Answer Book

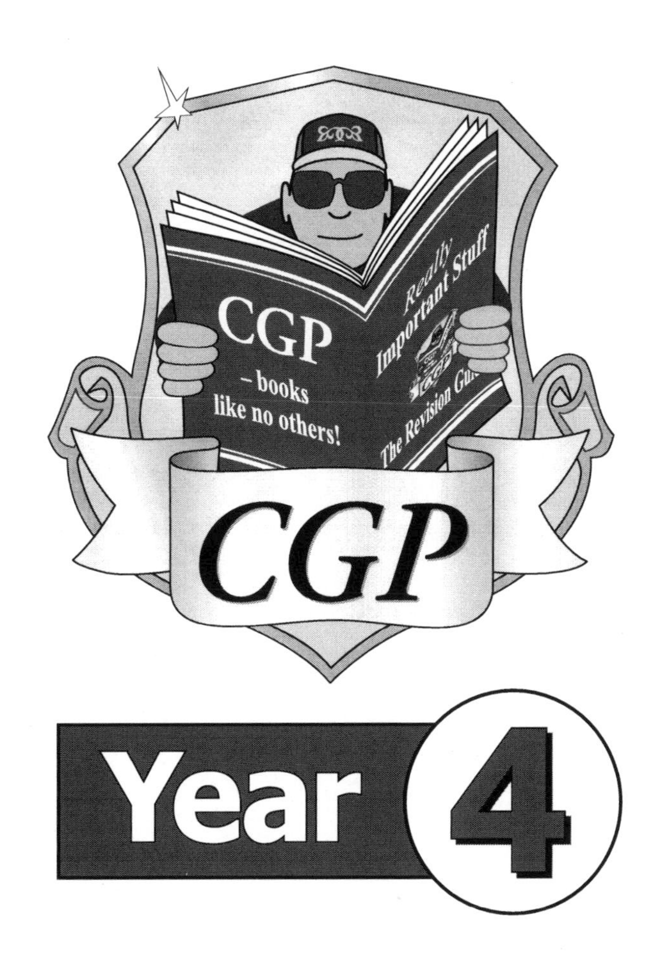


Year 4

Grammar • Punctuation • Spelling

# Contents

## Grammar



## Punctuation



## Spelling



Published by CGP

ISBN: 978 1 78294 151 4

www.cgpbooks.co.uk
Clipart from Corel®
Printed by Elanders Ltd, Newcastle upon Tyne.
Based on the classic CGP style created by Richard Parsons.

# Grammar

I don't eat meat, **but** I do eat fish.
We could go out, **or** we could stay in.

3. The runners are happy **because** they won the race.
   Let's get some petrol **before** we run out.
   We'll arrive on time **if** we hurry up.
   You can watch TV **unless** it's still broken.
4. I will wait **until** you arrive.
   **While** you were away, Jodie watered the plants.
   We missed our flight **because** we got stuck in traffic.
   **If** we can't get tickets, we'll watch the match on TV.
   **Since** he went away, we've had no one to play with.

*Pages 22 and 23 — Prepositions*

1. The teddy is **under** (or) **beneath** the table.
   The boy is **behind** the chair.
   The cat is **on** the chair.
   The lamp is **on** the table.
   The table is **next to** (or) **beside** (or) **by** the chair.
2. The waiter put flowers on the tables. — where
   I've been playing the violin since 2012. — when
   I hid behind the door to surprise him. — where
   He felt sick from eating too many sweets. — why
   I found the money after a good search. — when
   I can't go because of my dad's birthday. — why
3. Mike's been playing tennis **since** 10 o'clock this morning.
   You need to wash your hands **before** dinner.
   We played golf from 9 am **until** 12 pm.
   The film's almost finished — it's **near** the end.
   The referee handed out two red cards **during** the match.
4. Ollie lived in a house by the seaside.
   They left the presents on the table.
   I felt really tired after my swimming lesson.
   Andy ordered a pizza without cheese.
   We walked slowly towards the classroom.
   My cat loves to sleep in the laundry basket.
5. Any sentence that uses a preposition correctly.
   Examples:
   I left my homework **on the kitchen table.**
   We went for burgers **after the rugby match.**

## Section 5 — Verb Tenses

*Page 24 — Present Tense and Past Tense*

1.

| | | | | | | | | |
|---|---|---|---|---|---|---|---|---|
| M | K | Z | D | E | Y | Z | E | S |
| A | E | X | G | R | E | W | P | A |
| D | P | W | A | L | K | E | D | W |
| E | T | P | L | A | Y | E | D | R |
| Q | U | N | M | G | I | C | R | S |
| T | F | L | E | W | R | T | A | P |
| O | O | E | E | B | D | O | N | O |
| O | L | T | N | F | R | R | K | K |
| K | S | T | C | U | T | E | A | E |

2.

| Present Tense | Past Tense | Present Tense | Past Tense |
|---|---|---|---|
| I forget | I forgot | I read | I read |
| I appear | I appeared | I drive | I drove |
| I follow | I followed | I laugh | I laughed |
| I go | I went | I move | I moved |
| I wear | I wore | I give | I gave |

*Page 25 — Verbs with 'ing'*

1. Gerald **is speaking** Spanish.
   We **are sleeping** in our beds.
   I **am flying** to Africa.
   She **is lighting** a fire.
   They **are opening** a shop.
2. I am waiting.
   We were scratching.
   It was melting.
   They are jumping.

*Page 26 — Past Tense with 'have'*

1. cycled
   bought
   taken
   joined
2. He has broken the toy.
   She has played football today.
   I have caught a fish.

*Page 27 — Staying in the Same Tense*

1. You should have made these three sentences:
   I tore up my work and I threw it away so I got into trouble.
   I ride my bike every day because it keeps me fit and it's good fun.
   I am looking for clues and I am searching for a thief who is breaking the law.
2. When I was younger I **was** very shy. I **played** on my own. I did things by myself, until I **met** my best friend.

## Section 6 — Standard and Non-Standard English

*Pages 28 and 29 — Verb Agreement*

1. They are the best. — Standard
   They does the washing. — non-Standard
   I catch fish. — Standard
   You is wrong. — non-Standard
   I have a new bike. — Standard
   We is amazing! — non-Standard
   She write letters. — non-Standard
   You phones the school. — non-Standard
   He has one sister. — Standard

# Punctuation

2. You should have underlined and corrected these words:
   I is excited to see Kim. — am
   Horses jumps very high. — jump
   Alice rush things. — rushes
   You does too much. — do
3. I am writing a letter today.
   He wrote a letter last week.
   He has written a letter.
   I swept the floor yesterday.
   He sweeps the floor every day.
   I was sweeping the floor for ages.
4. You should have crossed out these words:
   I (~~been~~ / went) to visit my gran on Monday.
   Raj (saw / ~~seen~~) a pigeon yesterday.
   We have (been / ~~were~~) to the doctors today.
   I have (~~did~~ / done) my homework already.
   They (saw / ~~seen~~) where he went.
   Sarah has (done / ~~did~~) lots to help me.

*Pages 30 and 31 — Confusing Words*

1. I think ___ cakes needed longer in the oven. — these
   Go and ask ___ if they would like to come. — them
   Where shall I put ___ cardboard boxes? — these
   ___ clothes are far too big for me. — these
   I've told ___ to come home before tea time. — them
2. Fiona and ___ are going to the park later. — I
   ___ am baking a birthday cake for Daniel. — I
   The rabbits were happy to see Jo and ___ . — me
   Sarah is taking ___ to the pantomime. — me
   I need someone to help ___ with my maths. — me
   Sometimes Noah and ___ build tree houses. — I
   I don't think that's very fair on ___ . — me
3. Yes, **of** course you can.
   We must **have** left Finn behind.
   I might **have** worked it out.
   This could **have** gone wrong!
   Give two **of** those to Adam.
   You would **have** loved it.
   We'll be thinking **of** you.
   One cup **of** oats will do.
   They should **have** waited.
   I may **have** broken it.
4. You should have ticked these sentences:
   These maths tests have gone really well.
   Helen and I have finished our breakfast.
   We think we might have lost the car keys.
   These bananas need to be thrown away.

*Page 32 — Negatives*

1. You should have matched these pairs:
   I ain't going. — I'm not going.
   He ain't got much. — He hasn't got much.
   It ain't in here. — It isn't in here.
   You ain't trying. — You aren't trying.
2. You should have circled the underlined words and then matched them like this:
   You shouldn't never do that. — non-Standard
   I haven't got nothing to say. — non-Standard
   You mustn't talk to strangers. — Standard
   I didn't use none of the paints. — non-Standard
   Nobody did nothing to help. — non-Standard

## Punctuation

### Section 1 — Sentence Punctuation

*Pages 2 and 3 — Capital Letters and Full Stops*

1.

| Capital Letters | No Capital Letters |
|---|---|
| London Road | egg |
| Egypt | farmer |
| July | country |
| Thursday | city |
| Mr Holmes | palace |

2. You should have ticked:
   Last September, I visited my friend Lucy in Wales.
3. **L**ast **W**ednesday, we adopted a puppy from **M**r **M**arlow, our neighbour. **M**y brother wanted to call the puppy '**R**alph', but **I** wanted to name him '**B**enji'. **I**n the end, my mum named the puppy '**K**aspar'. **S**he says it's a popular name in **G**ermany.
4. Our teacher won the talent show.
   The cat jumped onto the table.
   He lost his new pair of gloves.
5. Any sentence which starts with a capital letter, has other capital letters where needed and ends with a full stop. Example:
   On Saturday, Emma and Robert went to Liverpool.

*Page 4 — Question Marks*

1. Harry thought about the strange boy who had moved in next door**.** What was his name**?** Where had he come from**?** Why was he so shy**?** Harry wanted to invite him to play football, but how could he if the boy never left his house**?** Harry decided that he would just have to knock on the door and introduce himself**.**
2. Any sensible sentence which starts with a capital letter and ends with a question mark. Examples:
   Where did you leave the key?
   When does the train leave?
   What did you get for your birthday?

# Punctuation

### Page 5 — Exclamation Marks

1. You should have ticked:
What a relief that is
We're saved
It's all your fault
I'm so excited
2. Any sensible sentence which starts with a capital letter and ends with an exclamation mark. Examples:
This noise is deafening!
That water is freezing!
I'm terrified of ghosts!

### Pages 6 and 7 — Sentence Practice

1. How did she find out — question mark
The book is about artists — full stop
Here I come, ready or not — exclamation mark
Would you like a cup of tea — question mark
Where are you going — question mark
Good gracious — exclamation mark
The beach was deserted — full stop
That's really not fair — exclamation mark
Why are the lights off — question mark
2. Help, this is an emergency**!**
What is two times three**?**
The jam is in the cupboard**.**
Wow, that's amazing**!**
Apples are red or green**.**
Why is the sea salty**?**
The thief had red hair**.**
Come on, slowcoach**!**
Who's the captain**?**
Where's Mum's bag**?**
Hey, come over here**!**
Delhi is in India**.**
3. **L**isbon is the capital city of **P**ortugal**.**
**H**elp, there's a monster under the bed**!**
**I**s **N**ew **Y**ork further away than **H**ong **K**ong**?**
**W**here are **M**r **W**hite and **M**rs **M**iller**?**
**H**ooray, it's the holidays at last**!**
4. Any three sentences, using each of the words, which start with a capital letter and end with either a full stop, a question mark or an exclamation mark.
Examples:
The secret agent crept along the corridor.
Do you want to be an astronaut when you grow up?
Stop that thief!

## Section 2 — Commas

### Pages 8 and 9 — Commas for Writing Lists

1. You will need eggs**,** flour and butter for this recipe.
I've been to Scotland**,** Ireland and Wales.
Iyla doesn't eat meat**,** fish or eggs.
I'd like a puppy**,** a pony or an iguana.
2. No running, shouting, splashing or diving!
I can add, subtract, multiply and divide.
There was cake, sweets, chocolate and biscuits.
You can have tea, coffee, hot chocolate or juice.
3. The chef chopped the carrots, peeled the potatoes, fried the onions and stirred the gravy.
At the funfair, Yasmin rode the dodgems, won a prize on the coconut shy, went on the Ferris wheel and ate some candy-floss.
4. Any sentence where commas are used correctly.
Examples:
Jordi is wearing a blue shirt, a pink tie, yellow trousers and green shoes.
After school, I usually watch TV, practise the clarinet, eat my dinner and read a chapter of my book.

### Pages 10 and 11 — Commas to Separate Clauses

1. You should have crossed these sentences:
Come and say goodbye, before you leave.
Dad orders pizza, when he doesn't want to cook.
We played outdoors, because it was sunny.
2. Because they're healthy**,** I eat lots of vegetables.
While we were waiting**,** we sang a song.
Even when it's snowing**,** Paula goes running.
If it rains**,** we'll go to the cinema instead.
3. As it's your birthday, I bought you a present.
Despite the fireworks, the puppy slept.
When the sun in shining, I'm happy.
While Sue cooked dinner, Andy walked the dog.
4. When you go abroad, you need to have a passport.
As it's the weekend, I'm allowed to stay up late.
If she goes swimming, Mary will need a towel.

### Pages 12 and 13 — Commas After Introductions

1. You should have ticked:
Behind the sofa, the cat is sleeping.
In the 1970s, flared trousers were popular.
You should have crossed:
In the, autumn the leaves turn red.
Despite the weather we went, for a walk.
2. In a large pan**,** melt the butter and syrup.
After that**,** stir in the oats.
With a wooden spoon**,** put the mixture into a baking tin and then put it in the oven.
After 30 minutes**,** take the flapjacks out.
3. Halfway down the road, she saw a cat.
At the wedding, there was a massive cake.
After a long wait, the bus finally arrived.
4. In Medieval England**,** many nobles lived in castles.
After that five-hour walk**,** I'm exhausted!
Every year**,** the drama group puts on a play.
In the flat next door**,** there's a lady with pink hair.
5. Any sentence where commas are used correctly.
Examples:
A week ago, I caught the train to Glasgow.
Under my brother's bed, there's a lot of mess.
After school, I always have a glass of juice.

# Punctuation

*Pages 14 and 15 — Comma Practice*

1. You should have ticked:
   In Australia, it is common for people to eat kangaroo meat!
   Although it was dark, Anjesh went for a run.
   Because he was snoring, we woke Dad up.
   These are the sentences you should have crossed, written out correctly:
   We went for a walk, played in the park and washed the dog.
   If she works hard at school, Tilly's gran will take her shopping.
   During the war, food was rationed.
   In the future, humans might live on Mars.
2. He ordered bacon, eggs, toast and sausages.
   In my village, there's a haunted house.
   While Mum drove, Dad read the map.
   Although it's boring, broccoli is very healthy.
3. You will need a ready-made pizza base, tomato sauce, mozzarella cheese and your choice of toppings.
   You could top your pizza with ham, pepperoni, olives or peppers.
   When you've finished adding the ingredients, the pizza can go in the oven. After about fifteen minutes, your pizza should be ready!

## Section 3 — Apostrophes

*Pages 16 and 17 — Apostrophes for Missing Letters*

1. You should have matched these pairs:
   what has — what's
   why is — why's
   we had — we'd
   you will — you'll
   must not — mustn't
2. You should have circled these words:
   should've
   When'll
   where's
   hadn't
   it'll
   he'd
3. You should have circled these words, and then written these pairs of words underneath them:
   I'm — I am
   She's — She is
   won't — will not
   we'll — we will
   isn't — is not
   you've — you have
   We're — We are
4. they have — they've
   she had — she'd
   we would — we'd
   it has — it's
   are not — aren't
   could have — could've
5. Any sentence where two words shortened with apostrophes are used correctly.
   Examples:
   Ask them and they'll tell you I didn't do it!

*Pages 18 and 19 — Apostrophes for Single Possession*

1. friend's
   business's
   scarf's
   actress's
2. camel's
   daisy's
   leaf's
   pizza's
   shed's
3. market's
   today's
   fairy's
   gnome's
   captain's
   island's
4. Lucas's pencil
   Emma's cow
   Hans's car
   Yasmin's snake

*Pages 20 and 21 — Apostrophes for Plural Possession*

1. You should have circled these phrases:
   two cakes' cases
   five cherries' stalks
2. the mice's home
   the men's toilets
   the feet's toes
   the children's pictures
3. You should have crossed out these phrases:
   the wives's
   the stories's
   the dice'
   the people'
4. You should have ticked these phrases:
   The fish's fins
   The rabbits' warrens
   The socks' heels
   The otters' dams
   The cushions' tassels
   The apples' stalks
   The leeks' stems

*Pages 22 and 23 — Its and It's*

1. You should have ticked these sentences:
   It's nice to sing carols at Christmas.
   The station sounded its alarm.
   It's good to have cereal for breakfast.

# Punctuation

2. You should have added apostrophes to these sentences:
   If I go to the shops, will you call me when it's ready?
   It's been so nice to see you.
3. You should have matched these pairs:
   It's been tiring — it has
   It's massive! — it is
   Its paw is muddy — belonging to it
4. This week, ___ been very wet. — it's
   The church rang ___ bells. — its
   ___ Thursday today. — it's
   The bank lost all ___ money. — its
   I don't like this because ___ tea. — it's
   The bird has built ___ nest. — its
5. It's been a wonderful holiday.
   The lizard flicked its tongue.
   It's so nice to be home at last.
   I love rugby because it's fun.
   Its eyes shone like stars.
   The goat looked at its horns.

*Pages 24 and 25 — Apostrophe Practice*

1.

| could not | couldn't |
|---|---|
| he has | he's |
| how is | how's |
| were not | weren't |
| are not | aren't |

| that will | that'll |
|---|---|
| might not | mightn't |
| would have | would've |
| we are | we're |
| he had | he'd |

2. The bananas' skins
   The pianos' pedals
   The gardens' roses
   The pencils' leads
   The pillows' feathers
   The books' pictures
3. for missing letters: it's better, that's a fact, he didn't, I couldn't
   to show possession: Meg's dad, Tim's bear, a mole's tunnel, the parrots' cage
4. it's
   Nikita's
   name's
   he's
   we'd
   dad's

## Section 4 — Inverted Commas

*Pages 26 and 27 — Punctuating Speech*

1. You should have added these commas:
   "You can't have any more," my aunt said.
   "Tonight there'll be a comet," said Mr Hoad.
   "I can play five instruments," said Tomek.
   "Sometimes I wear Mum's shoes," Fiona said.
   "We're going as far as the tree," said Peter.
2. Gemma said, "This is very wobbly jelly."
   Amelia thought, "I would love to visit Japan one day."
   Luis said, "Grapes can be purple or green."
   My dad said, "Let's make a list of everything we need."
   Jill thought, "I hope Jack has found some water by now."
   Stephen whispered, "I don't like mushy peas."
3. "I'm so tired ___" he said as he sat down. — comma
   Ivy said ___ "The train is ten minutes late." — comma
   "I hate brushing my hair," said Max ___ — full stop
   Nick said, "Gran is knitting me a cardigan ___" — full stop
   "Your kitten will be fine ___ " said the vet. — comma
   "It's taken us five years," said the builder ___ — full stop
   The teacher said ___ "Please sit quietly now." — comma
4. Felix said, "I support Manchester United."
   "I've made a daisy chain for you," said Holly.
   Aidan said, "This is my favourite book."
   "Now the rabbit will vanish," said the man.
   Heather said, "Here's the cake I made."

*Pages 28 and 29 — Punctuating Speech with ! or ?*

1. You should have ticked these sentences:
   "I don't want to go to bed yet!" yelled Mario.
   Sara asked, "Do you want to help us pick berries?"
   "Why are you rolling in the dirt?" my mum asked.
2. "Please can I paint my new bedroom orange?" asked Violet.
   "Don't you dare touch my new computer!" Jamie shouted.
   Rachel asked, "How long have you lived in this house?"
   The giant roared, "I smell the blood of an Englishman!"
   "Can I stay inside and play board games?" Josh asked.
3. "Will I get everything ready in time?" I **thought** to myself.
   "This is the best theme park ride ever!" **yelled** Scott.
   "Isaac Smith, put that down right now!" his mum **ordered**.
   "Oh, but why do I have to clean the cage?" **moaned** Max.
4. "Would you like to learn French?" asked Colin.
   I shouted, "Stop walking on my paintings!"
   "Where is a good place to eat?" we asked.
   Grace yelled, "Move out of my way now!"

## Section 5 — Paragraphs and Layout

*Pages 30 and 31 — Paragraphs*

1. You should have written three of these four reasons:
   When you're writing about a new time
   When you're writing about a new person
   When you're writing about a new subject
   When someone new speaks

# Spelling

2. You should have matched these pairs:
   My family tree is very complicated. — My mother has eight brothers and sisters.
   William Shakespeare is a famous writer. — He wrote lots of plays and some poetry.
   There are lots of good films out at the moment. — I'd like to see the one about the kids in space.
   Then, any sentence which is about learning things at school. Example:
   Today I learnt how to add up big numbers.
3. You should have added these paragraph markers:
   The swimming pool on Green Street is going to close. This will probably happen by Christmas. // "We are all very upset by the news because we will lose our jobs, and the people of this town will lose their lovely swimming pool," said a member of staff. // After the pool has closed, the nearest swimming centre will be an hour away in Jutton. This will be too far for many people. // "I won't be able to go to Jutton because I don't have a car, and there is no bus," said one elderly swimmer. "This means I won't be able to swim at all."
   You should have written these reasons:
   2nd paragraph: new person speaks
   3rd paragraph: new time
   4th paragraph: new person speaks
4. "Today, I learnt about paragraphs," said Rafiq.
   "Well done," said his gran. "Have some cake as a reward."

*Page 32 — Headings and Subheadings*

1. You should have written these labels:
   CLEANER WANTED — heading
   When and where? — subheading
   Who do I call? — subheading
2. You should have matched these pairs:
   Monday — We will start the week learning some cooking basics, including health and safety in the kitchen.
   Wednesday — By the middle of the week, you will have learnt to make simple and tasty meals for the whole family.
   Friday — At the end of the cookery course, we will learn to make the most difficult dishes.

## Spelling

### Section 1 — Prefixes

*Pages 2 and 3 — Prefixes — 'dis' and 'mis'*

1. **dis** + **order**, **mis** + **lead**, **dis** + **own**
2. **misprint**, **misshape**, **disobey**, **disregard**, **mistreat**
3. **dis**advantage, **dis**belief, **mis**hear, **mis**understand, **mis**calculated, **dis**connect, **mis**pronounced, **dis**appointed, **dis**honest
4. **mis**judge, **mis**spell, **mis**inform, **dis**appear, **dis**agree
5. **misuse**, **dislike**

*Pages 4 and 5 — Prefixes — 'in' 'il' 'im' and 'ir'*

1. **in** + **correct**, **il** + **legible**, **im** + **polite**, **in** + **formal**, **in** + **direct**, **im** + **pure**
2. **immortal**, **inoffensive**, **irreparable**, **inadequate**
3. **incapable**, **impossible**, **irrational**, **illogical**
4. **ineffective**, **irregular**, **invalid**, **improper**, **illegal**
5. **im**patient, **in**accurate, **ir**resistible, **il**logical, **ir**responsible

*Pages 6 and 7 — Prefixes — 're' 'anti' and 'auto'*

1. **anti**climax, **re**design, **auto**pilot, **anti**biotic, **re**appear, **re**emerge, **re**open, **anti**septic, **re**fresh
2. **anticlockwise**, **remarried**, **autograph**, **resend**, **antivirus**, **rephrase**
3. **reapply**, **automobile**, **redecorate**, **antisocial**, **rearrange**
4. Fred is writing his **autobiography**.
   I need to **redo** my homework because it got wet.
   **Return** the form in the envelope provided.
   In winter, people use **antifreeze** spray on their cars.
   Mrs Potter **reheats** her leftover meals in the microwave.

*Pages 8 and 9 — Prefixes — 'sub' 'super' and 'inter'*

1. **sublet**, **subtotal**, **superglue**
2. **supernatural**, **interrelated**, **interlock**, **superpower**, **submerge**
3. **inter**active, **inter**city, **Sub**headings, **super**glue, **super**star, **super**man, **sub**divided
4. **submarine**, **supermarket**
5. Any sentence where the word is used correctly. Examples:
   I need to think of a **subtitle** for my project.
   If I were a **superhero**, I would be able to turn invisible.
   Ronald booked an **international** flight to Canada.

### Section 2 — Suffixes and Word Endings

*Pages 10 and 11 — Suffixes — Double Letters*

1. You should have ticked: **preferred**, **offering**, **equipped**.
   You should have crossed: **prefered**, **offerring**, **equiped**.
2. Double letter: swim**ming**, run**ning**, stop**ping**, begin**ning**
   No double letter: jump**ing**, play**ing**, garden**ing**
3. **limited**, **cancelled**, **jumped**, **singing**
4. **beginner**, **gardener**, **hotter**, **swimmer**
5. You should have circled: **traveled**, **visitted**, **regreted**, **poping**, **feelling**
   The correct spellings are: **travelled**, **visited**, **regretted**, **popping**, **feeling**

# Spelling

## Pages 12 and 13 — Suffixes — 'ation' and 'ous'

1. **donation**, **dangerous**, **creation**, **expectation**, **glamorous**
2. You should have underlined: **couragous**, **humourous**, **infectous**, **senseation**.
   The correct spellings are: **courageous**, **humorous**, **infectious**, **sensation**.
3. relax**ation**, outrage**ous**, inform**ation**
4. **poisonous**, **humorous**, **mountainous**
5. You should have circled: **prepareations**, **celebrateions**, **inviteations**, **fameous**, **locatetion**, **indicatetions**.
   The correct spellings are: **preparations**, **celebrations**, **invitations**, **famous**, **location**, **indications**.

## Pages 14 and 15 — Suffixes — 'ly'

1. **sadly**, **doubly**, **gladly**, **subtly**, **safely**, **quickly**, **cuddly**
2.

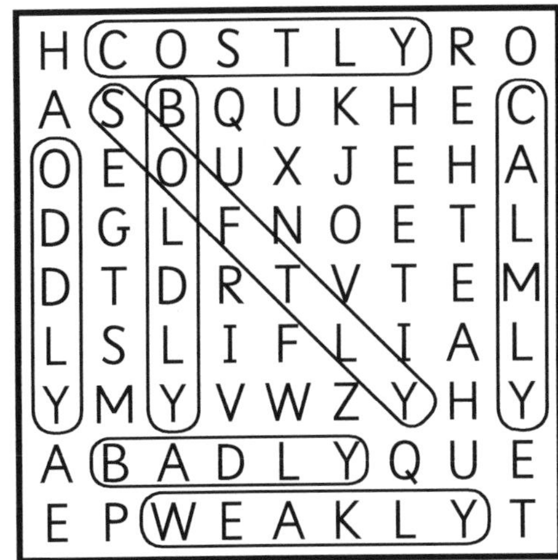


3. **frantically**, **completely**, **gently**, **truly**, **fiddly**, **nobly**
4. happy — **happily**, simple — **simply**, dead — **deadly**, easy — **easily**, busy — **busily**, angry — **angrily**
5. Any sentence where the word is used correctly.
   Examples:
   Jason **comically** pulled a funny face.
   Although he was an hour late, Callum **finally** arrived.

## Pages 16 and 17 — Word Endings — 'sure' and 'ture'

1. **pressure**, **literature**, **furniture**, **leisure**, **torture**
2. **enclosure**, **adventure**, **mixture**, **manufacture**, **exposure**, **composure**, **gesture**
3. **treasure**, **picture**, **enclosure**, **temperature**, **signature**
4. reas**sure**, struc**ture**, mois**ture**, mea**sure**, clo**sure**
5. Any words ending in -sure or -ture that are spelt correctly.
   Examples:
   **unsure**, **assure**, **ensure**, **insure**, **closure**, **pressure**
   **posture**, **nurture**, **vulture**, **venture**, **fracture**

## Pages 18 and 19 — Word Endings — The 'shun' Sound

1. You should have ticked: **permission**, **division**, **mention**.
   You should have crossed: **politition**, **complecian**, **attencian**, **hesitacian**, **musicsion**, **confesion**.
   The correct spellings are: **politician**, **completion**, **attention**, **hesitation**, **musician**, **confession**.
2. **expression**, **reduction**, **electrician**, **direction**, **discussion**, **confusion**, **technician**
3. Across: 1. **mathematician** 2. **injection**
   3. **invitation** 4. **television**
   Down: 1. **magician** 2. **invention**

## Pages 20 and 21 — Word Endings — 'gue' and 'que'

1. You should have underlined: **catalog**, **dialog**, **intrig**
   The correct spellings are: **catalogue**, **dialogue**, **intrigue**
2. You should have underlined: **grotesk**, **technik**, **boutik**, **unik**.
   The correct spellings are: **grotesque**, **technique**, **boutique**, **unique**.
3. clun**g**, pla**gue**, stron**g**, merin**gue**
4. anti**que**, ban**k**, criti**que**, drin**k**
5. **cheque**, **tongue**
6. Any sentence where a word ending in gue or que is used correctly.
   Examples:
   Jean received a **plaque** for winning the competition.
   I felt really tired — I was overcome by **fatigue**.

# Section 3 — Confusing Words

## Page 22 — The Short 'i' Sound

1. You should have circled: **Egypt**, **witch**, **myth**, **gym**
2. You should have ticked: **sympathy**, **satisfy**
   You should have crossed: **sistem**, **rapyd**, **abolysh**, **phisics**
   The correct spellings are: **system**, **rapid**, **abolish**, **physics**
3. **mistakes**, **symbols**

## Page 23 — The Short 'u' Sound

1. **umbrella**, **touch**
2. **double**, **nothing**, **Rough**, **brother**, **cousin**
3. Any sentence where the word is used correctly.
   Examples:
   Spain is a **country** in Europe.
   He looks too **young** to be at university.
   There isn't **enough** for everyone.

## Page 24 — The Hard 'c' Sound

1. **leak**, **chord**, **brick**, **smoke**, **electric**
2. **ch**aos, awa**k**e, **ch**emist, an**ch**or, **ch**aracter, **k**ettle, tri**ck**, **c**are, e**ch**o, sti**ck**
3. **mechanic**, **calendar**, **soccer**, **chorus**

0118 — 16943

# Spelling

*Page 25 — The Soft 'c' Sound*

1. **consent**, **science**, **recipe**, **crescent**
2. You should have underlined: **prinsce**, **parscel**, **deside**, **decend**, **suspence**
   The correct spellings are: **prince**, **parcel**, **decide**, **descend**, **suspense**
3. Any sentence where the word is used correctly.
   Examples:
   **Discipline** and restraint are good qualities.
   The special effects **fascinate** me.
   There was a very strange **scent** in the air.
   Let me set the **scene** for you.

*Page 26 — The 'sh' Sound*

1. wi**sh**, poli**sh**, **ch**arade, radi**sh**, **ch**ivalry, pre**ss**ure, **sh**immer, **sh**adow, para**ch**ute
2. **ch**ef, bro**ch**ure, **s**ure, ma**ch**ine, pari**sh**
3. Any sentence where the word is used correctly.
   Examples:
   I need to **insure** my new car.
   He has committed a crime and we must **punish** him.
   I think my dad's **moustache** is impressive.

*Page 27 — The 'ay' Sound*

1. You should have circled: **obay**, **veighl**, **neibour**, **shaike**
   The correct spellings are: **obey**, **veil** or **vale**, **neighbour**, **shake**
2. **afraid**, **freight**, **hesitate**
3. **plain**, **eight**

*Pages 28 and 29 — Plurals and Apostrophes*

1. You should have ticked: **The witches' cauldrons**, **The women's handbags**
2. men**'s**, deer**'s**, beaches**'**, cats**'**
3. You should have underlined: **the elves' hats**, **the companies' employees**, **the ladies' coats**, **the boxes' labels**, **the policemen's handcuffs**, **the calves' mothers**
4. **The students' books**
   **The children's toys**
   **The snowmen's scarves**
5. More than one shoe belonging to more than one girl — **The girls' shoes**
   One shoe belonging to one girl — **The girl's shoe**
   One shoe belonging to more than one girl — **The girls' shoe**
6. Any sentence that uses possessive apostrophes correctly.
   Examples:
   The mice**'s** mother watched carefully for the cat.
   Snakes**'** tongues are very long.
   The geese**'s** wings helped them to fly.

*Pages 30 to 32 — Homophones*

1. You should have matched: **piece** with "part of something", **peace** with "calm and quiet", **plain** with "simple or ordinary", **plane** with "a flying vehicle".
2. **aisle**, **Isle**, **I'll**
3. You should have circled: **ate**, **air**, **dear**
   The correct spellings are: **eight**, **heir**, **deer**
4. **He'll** definitely be late.
   Shoes that don't fit properly often rub on the **heel**.
   I hope my injury will **heal** soon.
5. **seen**, **fair**, **flea**, **need**, **mist**, **knot**
6. **grate**, **great**
7. **which** / **witch**, **so** / **sew**, **tail** / **tale**, **stare** / **stair**, **new** / **knew**, **quay** / **key**
8. Any sentence where the word is used correctly.
   Examples:
   **Blue** is my favourite colour.
   I **blew** the whistle to end the game.
   Jim heard a loud **groan**.
   You can buy expensive clothes when you are fully **grown**.

Do not use while feeding lions

ISBN 978 1 78294 151 4
9 781782 941514

E4SA21
£2.00
(Retail Price)

www.cgpbooks.co.uk